A Mail Carrier's Busy Day

Written and Illustrated by Read With You
Center for Excellence in STEAM Education

Read With You

Published by Read With You Publishing. Printed in the United States of America.

Read With You and associated logos are trademarks and/or registered trademarks of Read With You L.L.C.

ISBN-13: 979-8-88618-319-1

First Edition October 2022

Hi! I'm Theo.
I am a mail carrier.

I deliver the mail.
I bring letters, postcards,
and packages!

One day, I go to work.
I see a robot in the mailroom.

"This is Mailbot," Mr. Mac says.
"He delivers the mail now."

"But what about me?" I ask.
"You are fired," Mr. Mac says.

"But I am better!" I shout.
"Mailbot is faster,"
Mr. Mac says.

"Let us race," I say.
"I will show you!"

I jump on my bike.
I grab my mailbag.

Mailbot gets ready.
He grabs his mailbag.

"Three... two... one... GO!" Mr. Mac shouts.
Mailbot and I race.

First, we go to Suzy's house.
Mailbot flies ahead!

He tosses her newspaper through the window. "Oh, no!" Suzy cries.

I place Suzy's package
by her door.
"Thank you!" Suzy says.

Next, we go to Rue's house.
Mailbot flies ahead!

He throws Rue's package into
her rose bush.
"Yikes!" Rue says.

I set Rue's newspaper
on her porch.
"Thanks!" Rue says.

Last, we go to Paul's house. Mailbot flies ahead!

Mailbot flings a letter
into the pool.
"Oh, no!" Paul shouts.

I drop the postcard
into the mailbox.
"Thanks!" Paul says.

We finish our route.
Mailbot is much faster.

"Mailbot wins!" Mr. Mac says. "He is the town's new mail carrier."

I sigh. I feel sad.
I give Mr. Mac my hat
and bag.

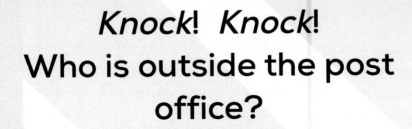

Knock! *Knock*!
Who is outside the post office?

"Mailbot broke my window!"
Suzy cries.
"Mailbot smashed my roses!"
Rue shouts.

"Mailbot threw my letter in the pool," Paul says.
"I cannot read it."

"Oh, dear," Mr. Mac says. "Mailbot is not a good mail carrier."

"Theo, you are the best!" Mr. Mac says.
Hooray! I am the town's mail carrier.

Answer

- What is Theo's job?

- Why does Theo race Mailbot?

- Who is faster: Theo or Mailbot?

- Who is a better mail carrier: Theo or Mailbot?

Learn

This book is filled with words related to being a **mail carrier**! Look at the list below. Do you know what these words mean?

- letter
- postcard
- package
- mailroom
- to deliver
- route

Can you think of any other words related to mail carriers? Hint: think of words with *post*.

Act

Pretend to be a mail carrier! First, decide what you will deliver to the people in your home. It could be a snack, a nice letter, or a surprise! Then, plan your route. Are the people in your household surprised? How do they think you did?

Discover

Did you know that in the United States, over 36 million packages are delivered each day?! That is a great deal of packages! How many packages do you get in your household per week? What is often in these packages? If you aren't sure, ask an adult!

Made in the USA
Coppell, TX
17 April 2023

15689169R00021